Gracie to the Rescue

The life and adventures of a rescue dog

by Katie Rynkiewich and Edgar Ramirez

Illustrated by Gian Silva

To our little one, we cannot wait to meet you.
This is for you.

Gracie to the Rescue

The life and adventures of a rescue dog

My name is Gracie.

When I was young I lived in Colorado.

I loved the snow! Sometimes,
I would run through the snow to fetch
my precious pink ball.

I loved my toys. I loved my food.
I loved my bed. I loved my house.

I never followed any rules.
I was very naughty. I loved my family,
but I did not know how to show it.

One day, my family came home with a baby. I complained, "I was here first!" My family loved the baby. The baby was all they talked about.

I barked to get their attention, but my daddy said, "Bad Gracie!". My family gave me up for adoption when I was 6 years old.

I was fostered by a nice lady in Missouri. There, I lived with really big dogs. I could not find a spot. The big dogs were everywhere!

I hid under the bed, "You can't find me in here!" I told the big dogs.
It was lonely under the bed.

The day my new mommy and daddy came
to rescue me I rolled over onto their feet,
"Please pet me!" I said. My new mommy and
daddy laughed and gave me
the most wonderful pets.

I was 8 years old when I was rescued by my new mommy and daddy.

My new daddy had to stop me from going under the bed all the time. Sometimes, I got scared and angry. My new mommy and daddy loved me, but they were hurt by my behavior.

My new mommy and daddy helped me understand that I do not need to be scared, that I can ask for things nicely, and that I can love and be loved.

I am a happy dog. Now I share my toys. Now I wait for my food. Now, I get to play with the precious pink ball again.

I love my family. My mommy and daddy rescued me and I rescued them.

Gracie is 13 years young and, as we write this, she is resting on the couch. A few weeks ago, we bought her steps since she can no longer jump up to her spot. Her little back legs are not as strong as they used to be, but her spirit is intact.

Rescuing our Gracie has been the biggest adventure of our lives. If you are looking to adopt, get to know different dogs and ask the organization or foster parent as many questions as you can. After all, the dog is new for you and you are new for the dog.

We hope this book inspires people to embark on their own journeys of adoption.

Made in United States
North Haven, CT
12 January 2022

14694720R00015